CU00705495

11+ 3D Non-verbal Reasoning

BOOK 2

Topic Tests and Mixed Tests

How to use this pack to make the most of 11 plus exam preparation

It is important to remember that for 11 plus exams there is no national syllabus, no pass mark and no retake option! It is therefore vitally important that your child is fully primed in order to perform to the best of their ability to give themselves the best possible chance on the day.

Unlike similar publications, the First Past the Post® series uniquely assesses your child's performance on a question-by-question basis, helping to identify areas for improvement and providing suggestions for further targeted tests.

3D Non-Verbal Reasoning

This series of mini-tests is representative of the non-verbal reasoning section of contemporary multi-disciplinary 11 plus tests, which typically have two papers containing around a dozen questions each. The suggested time is based on classroom testing sessions held at our centre.

Never has it been more useful to learn from mistakes!

Students can improve by as much as 15% not only by focused practice but also by targeting any weak areas.

How to manage your child's practice

To get the most up-to-date information log on to the Eleven Plus Exams website (www.elevenplusexams.co.uk). Eleven Plus Exams is the largest UK based online resource with over 40,000 webpages and a forum administered by a select group of experienced moderators.

About the authors

The Eleven Plus Exams **First Past the Post®** series has been created by a team of experienced tutors and authors from leading British universities including Oxford and Cambridge.

Published by University of Buckingham Press

With special thanks to all the children who tested our material at the Eleven Plus Exams centre in Harrow.

ISBN: 9781908684479

elevenplusexams
head for success

Copyright © ElevenPlusExams.co.uk 2014

All rights reserved. No part of this publication may be reproduced, stored or introduced into a retrieval system or transmitted in any form or by any means, without the prior written permission of the publisher nor may be circulated in any form of binding or cover other than the one it was published and without a similar condition including this condition being imposed on the subsequent publisher.

BLANK PAGE

Contents Page

This workbook comprises tests. The first four are specific to each individual style of 3D NVR questions, made up of twenty-four questions each. Each is intended to take twelve minutes to complete. The final four tests are mixed papers encompassing all four styles of 3D NVR questions. They are made up of twenty-one questions each and should take eleven minutes to complete.

Once you have completed each test mark it using the answers provided at the back of the book. Upload your results anonymously onto our 11+ Peer Compare System™ to see how well you performed in comparison to others who have taken the same test.

You can register by visiting www.ElevenPlusExams.co.uk/FirstPastThePost to post your results anonymously and obtain feedback.

FIRST PAST THE POST® SERIES

3D Non-Verbal Reasoning

Paper 1 - 3D Views

Page	2	3	4	5	Total
Mark	/6	/6	/6	/6	/24

Read the following instructions carefully:

1. You have **12 minutes** to complete this test of **24 questions**.

2. Work as quickly and carefully as you can.

3. Once you have finished a page go straight onto the next page until you finish the test.

4. To change an answer, rub out your original answer and mark your new answer clearly.

5. If you are unsure of the answer, choose the one you think is most appropriate or return to it later.

6. Once you have completed the paper go back to any questions you have missed out and check your answers.

Good luck!

After you have finished this paper you can use the 11+ Peer Compare System™ to see how well you performed in comparison to others who have taken this test. You can register by visiting www.ElevenPlusExams.co.uk/FirstPastThePost to post your results anonymously and obtain the feedback.

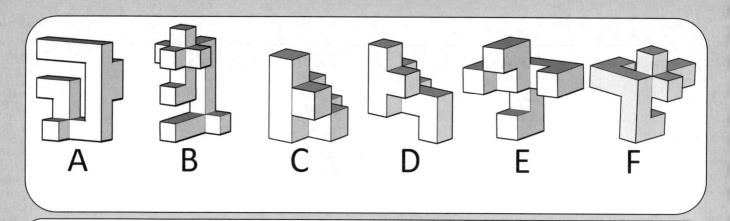

A B C D E F

3D Views

Identify which shape has been rotated by placing a mark in the box next to its corresponding letter, or mark 'None'.

1.

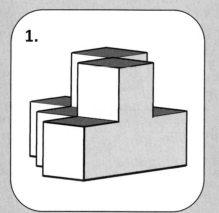

A ☐ D ☐

B ☐ E ☐

C ☐ F ☐

None ☐

2.

A ☐ D ☐

B ☐ E ☐

C ☐ F ☐

None ☐

3.

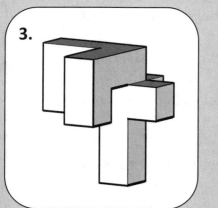

A ☐ D ☐

B ☐ E ☐

C ☐ F ☐

None ☐

4.

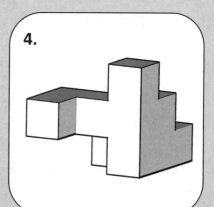

A ☐ D ☐

B ☐ E ☐

C ☐ F ☐

None ☐

5.

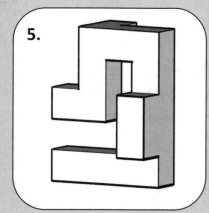

A ☐ D ☐

B ☐ E ☐

C ☐ F ☐

None ☐

6.

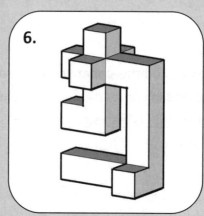

A ☐ D ☐

B ☐ E ☐

C ☐ F ☐

None ☐

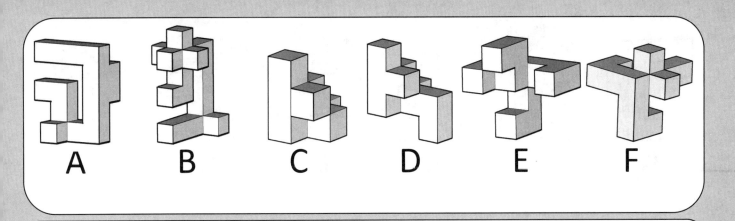

3D Views

Identify which shape has been rotated by placing a mark in the box next to its corresponding letter, or mark 'None'.

7.

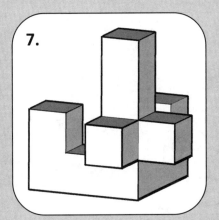

A ☐   D ☐

B ☐   E ☐

C ☐   F ☐

None ☐

8.

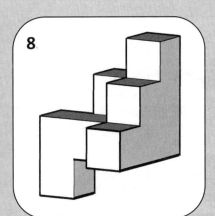

A ☐   D ☐

B ☐   E ☐

C ☐   F ☐

None ☐

9.

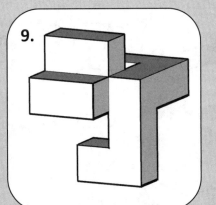

A ☐   D ☐

B ☐   E ☐

C ☐   F ☐

None ☐

10.

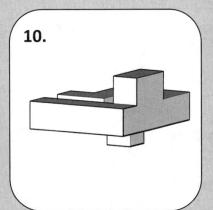

A ☐   D ☐

B ☐   E ☐

C ☐   F ☐

None ☐

11.

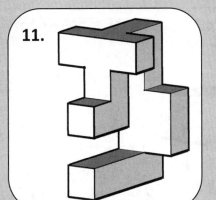

A ☐   D ☐

B ☐   E ☐

C ☐   F ☐

None ☐

12.

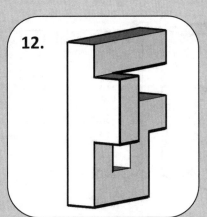

A ☐   D ☐

B ☐   E ☐

C ☐   F ☐

None ☐

© 2014 ElevenPlusExams.co.uk   -3-   COPYING STRICTLY PROHIBITED

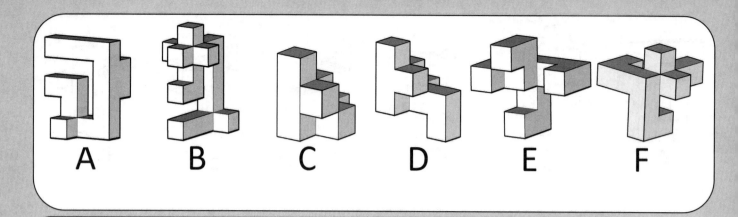

A　　B　　C　　D　　E　　F

3D Views

Identify which shape has been rotated by placing a mark in the box next to its corresponding letter, or mark 'None'.

13.

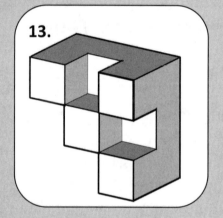

A ▢　D ▢

B ▢　E ▢

C ▢　F ▢

None ▢

14.

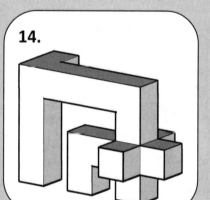

A ▢　D ▢

B ▢　E ▢

C ▢　F ▢

None ▢

15.

A ▢　D ▢

B ▢　E ▢

C ▢　F ▢

None ▢

16.

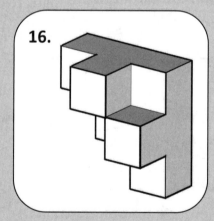

A ▢　D ▢

B ▢　E ▢

C ▢　F ▢

None ▢

17.

A ▢　D ▢

B ▢　E ▢

C ▢　F ▢

None ▢

18.

A ▢　D ▢

B ▢　E ▢

C ▢　F ▢

None ▢

© 2014 ElevenPlusExams.co.uk　　-4-　　COPYING STRICTLY PROHIBITED

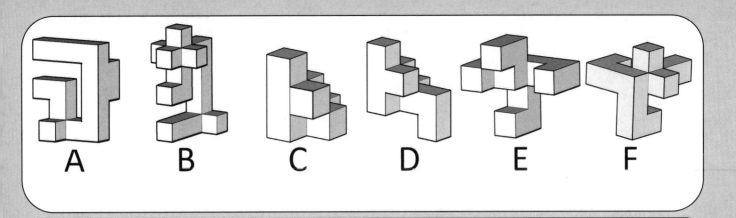

A   B   C   D   E   F

3D Views

Identify which shape has been rotated by placing a mark in the box next to its corresponding letter, or mark 'None'.

19.

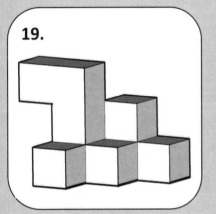

A ☐   D ☐

B ☐   E ☐

C ☐   F ☐

None ☐

20.

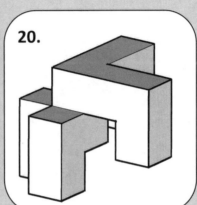

A ☐   D ☐

B ☐   E ☐

C ☐   F ☐

None ☐

21.

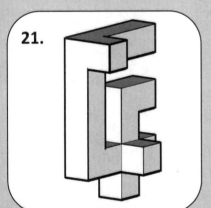

A ☐   D ☐

B ☐   E ☐

C ☐   F ☐

None ☐

22.

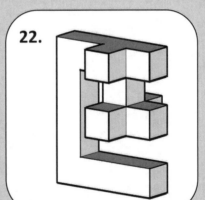

A ☐   D ☐

B ☐   E ☐

C ☐   F ☐

None ☐

23.

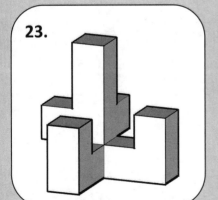

A ☐   D ☐

B ☐   E ☐

C ☐   F ☐

None ☐

24.

A ☐   D ☐

B ☐   E ☐

C ☐   F ☐

None ☐

BLANK PAGE

© 2014 ElevenPlusExams.co.uk   COPYING STRICTLY PROHIBITED

FIRST PAST THE POST® SERIES

3D Non-Verbal Reasoning
Paper 2 - 3D Composite Shapes

Page	8	9	10	11	12	Total
Mark	/5	/5	/5	/5	/4	/24

Read the following instructions carefully:

1. You have **12 minutes** to complete this test of **24 questions**.

2. Work as quickly and carefully as you can.

3. Once you have finished a page go straight onto the next page until you finish the test.

4. To change an answer, rub out your original answer and mark your new answer clearly.

5. If you are unsure of the answer, choose the one you think is most appropriate or return to it later.

6. Once you have completed the paper go back to any questions you have missed out and check your answers.

Good luck!

After you have finished this paper you can use the 11+ Peer Compare System[TM] to see how well you performed in comparison to others who have taken this test. You can register by visiting www.ElevenPlusExams.co.uk/FirstPastThePost to post your results anonymously and obtain the feedback.

3D Composite Shapes

Work out which set of blocks can be put together to make the 3D figure on the left.

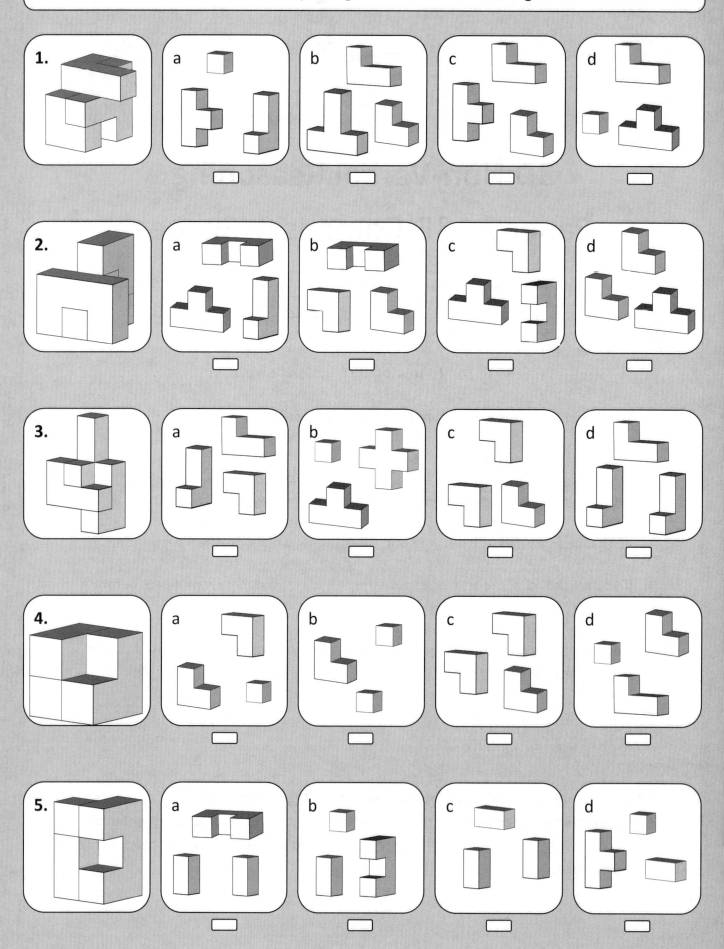

3D Composite Shapes

Work out which set of blocks can be put together to make the 3D figure on the left.

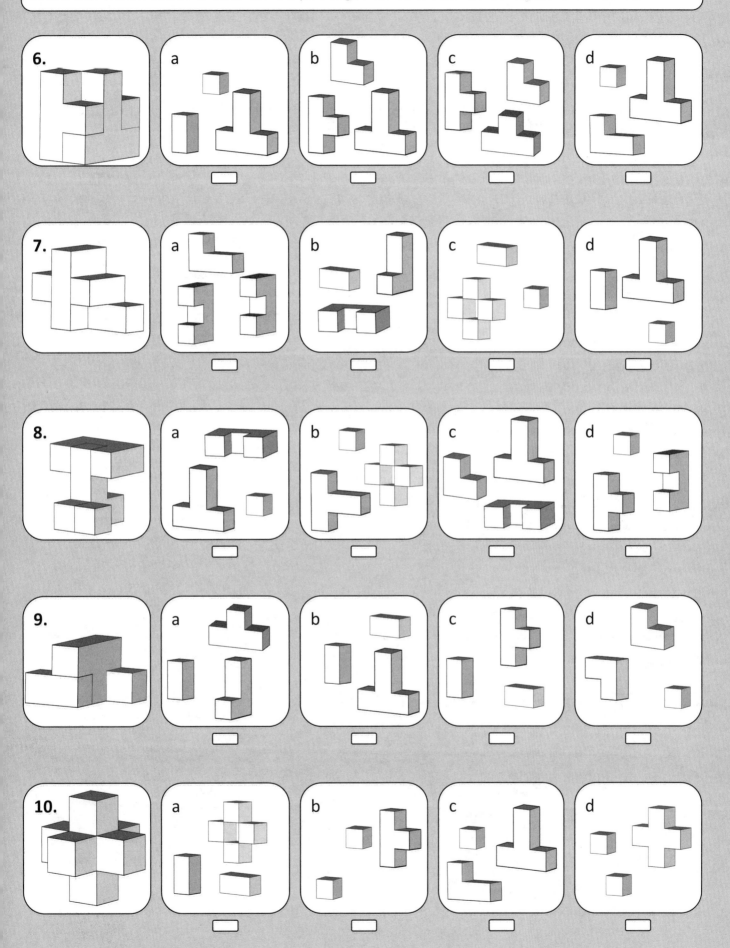

6.   a   b   c   d

7.   a   b   c   d

8.   a   b   c   d

9.   a   b   c   d

10.   a   b   c   d

3D Composite Shapes

Work out which set of blocks can be put together to make the 3D figure on the left.

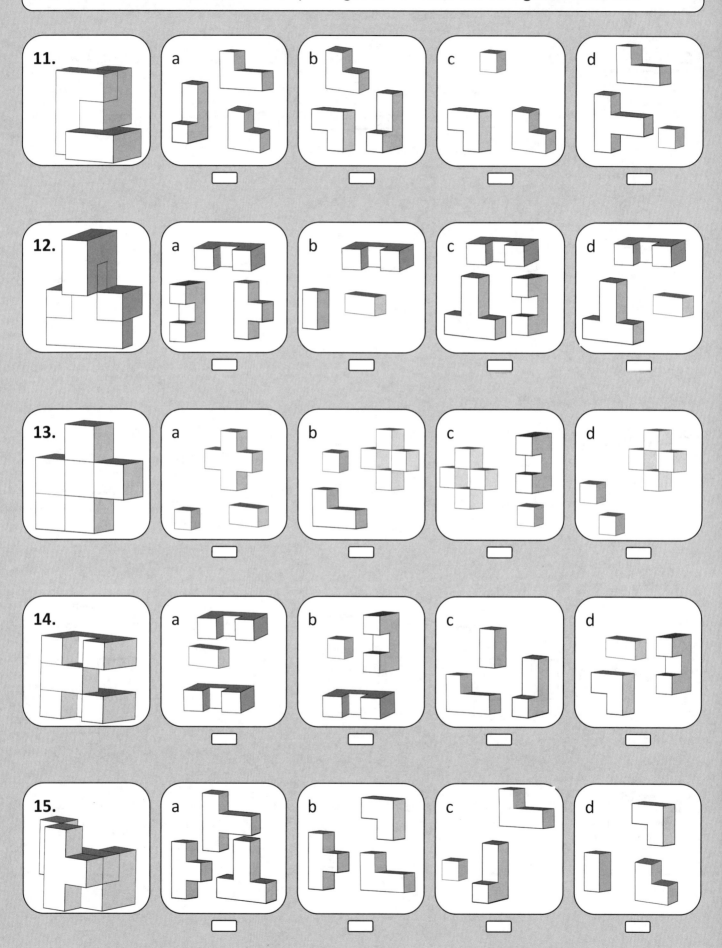

3D Composite Shapes

Work out which set of blocks can be put together to make the 3D figure on the left.

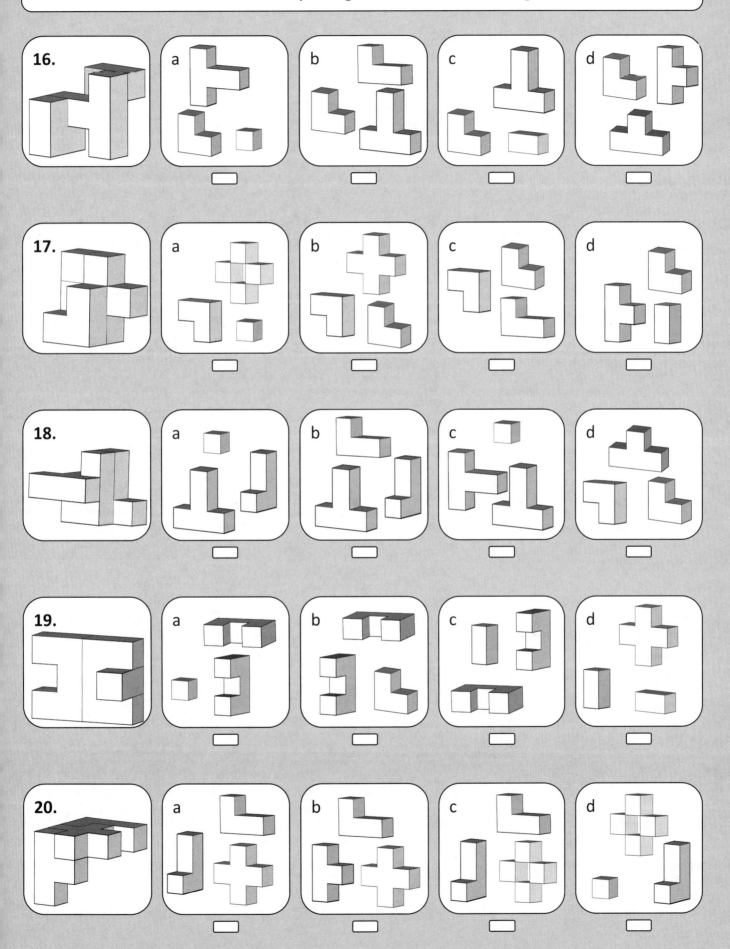

16.   a   b   c   d

17.   a   b   c   d

18.   a   b   c   d

19.   a   b   c   d

20.   a   b   c   d

3D Composite Shapes

Work out which set of blocks can be put together to make the 3D figure on the left.

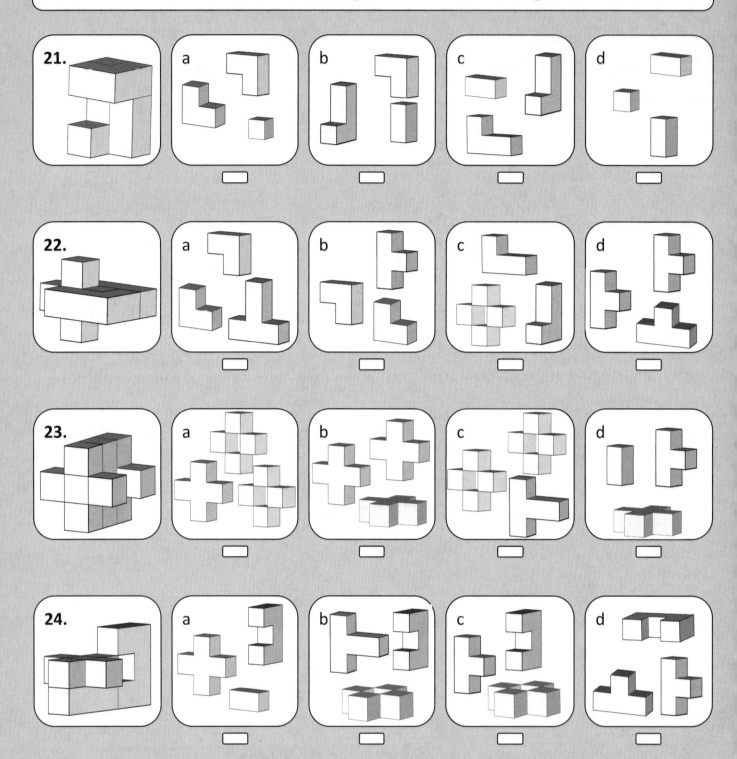

FIRST PAST THE POST® SERIES

3D Non-Verbal Reasoning

Paper 3 - 3D Cube Nets

Page	14	15	16	17	18	Total
Mark	/5	/5	/5	/5	/4	/24

Read the following instructions carefully:

1. You have **12 minutes** to complete this test of **24 questions**.

2. Work as quickly and carefully as you can.

3. Once you have finished a page go straight onto the next page until you finish the test.

4. To change an answer, rub out your original answer and mark your new answer clearly.

5. If you are unsure of the answer, choose the one you think is most appropriate or return to it later.

6. Once you have completed the paper go back to any questions you have missed out and check your answers.

Good luck!

After you have finished this paper you can use the 11+ Peer Compare System™ to see how well you performed in comparison to others who have taken this test. You can register by visiting www.ElevenPlusExams.co.uk/FirstPastThePost to post your results anonymously and obtain the feedback.

3D Cube Nets

Work out which of the four cubes can be made from the net.

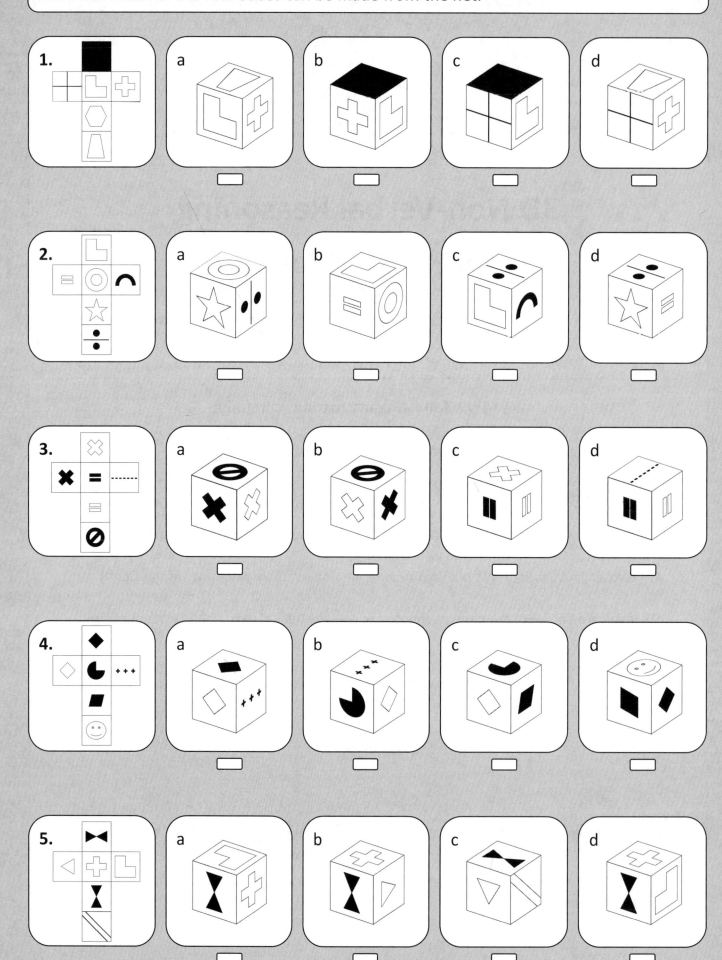

3D Cube Nets

Work out which of the four cubes can be made from the net.

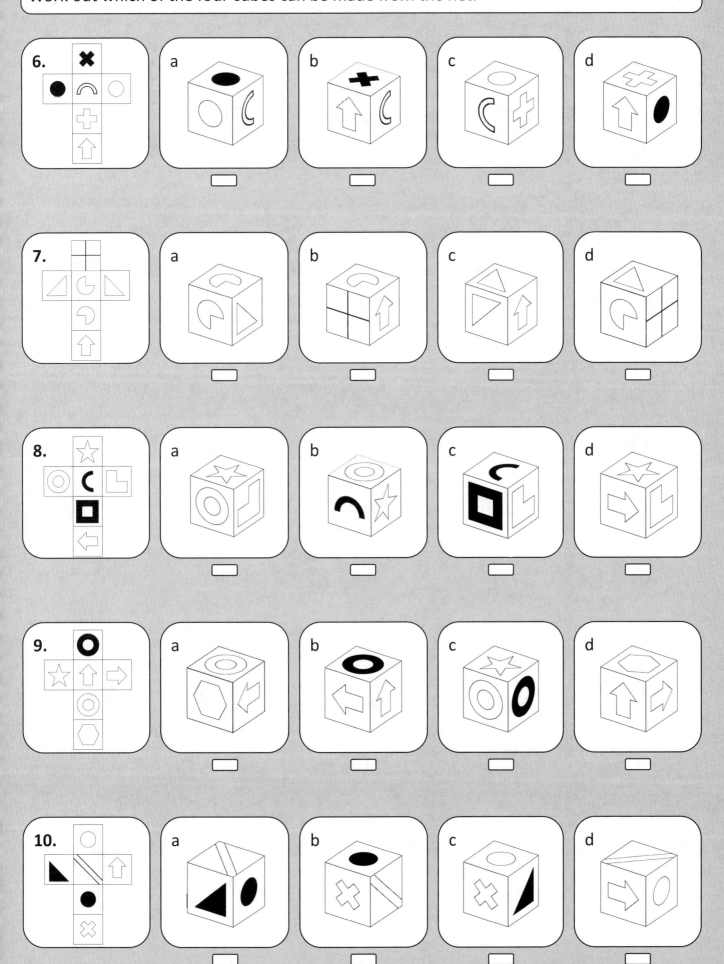

3D Cube Nets

Work out which of the four cubes can be made from the net.

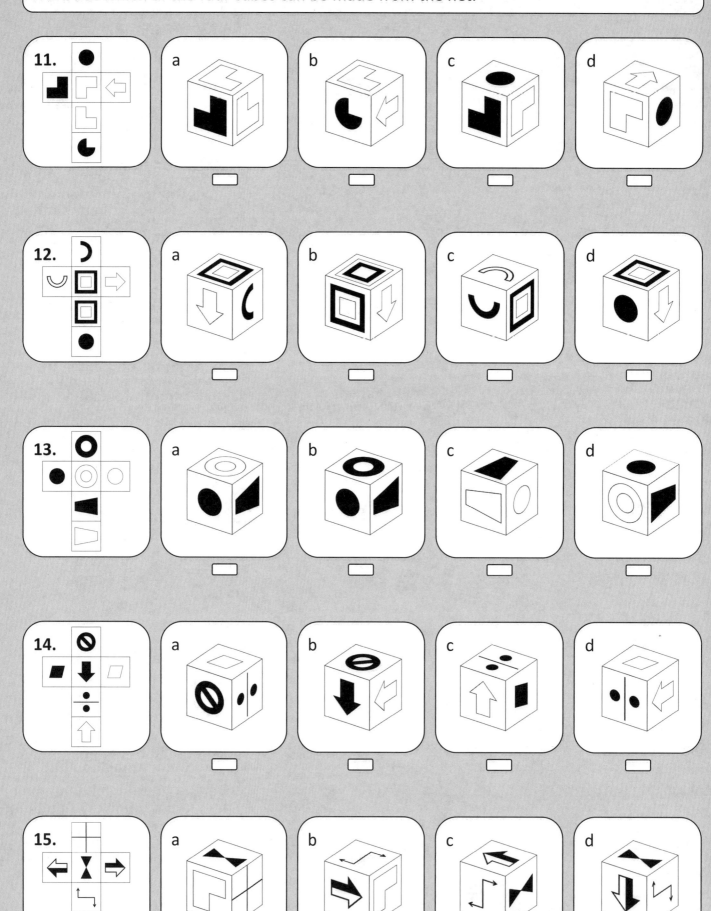

3D Cube Nets

Work out which of the four cubes can be made from the net.

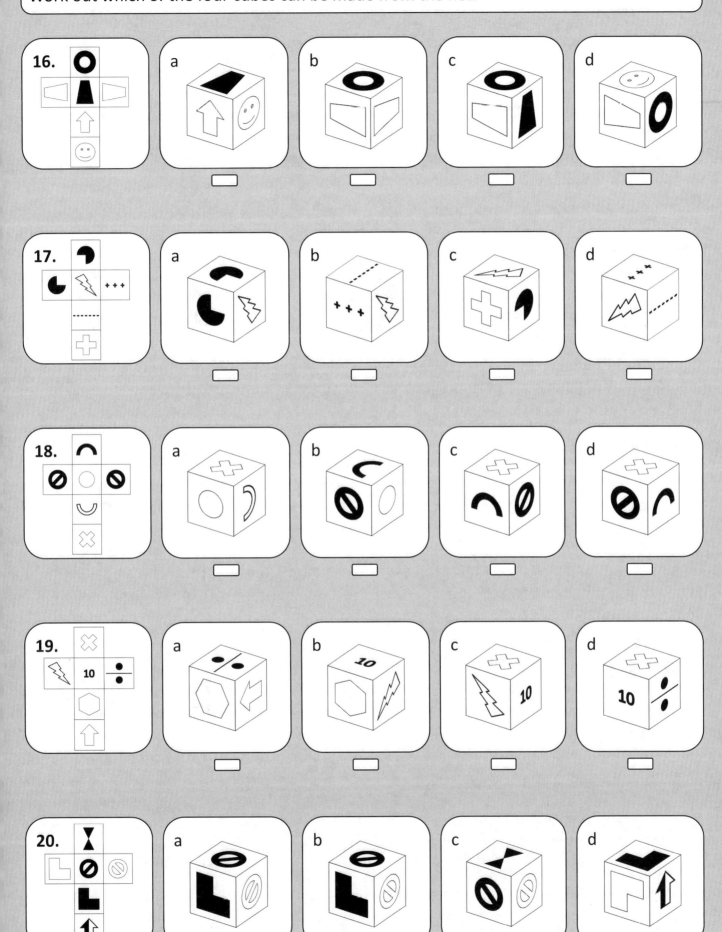

3D Cube Nets

Work out which of the four cubes can be made from the net.

21.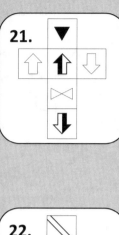

a

b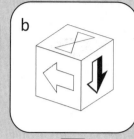

c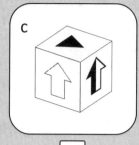

d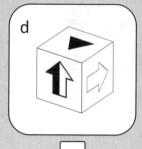

22.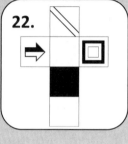

a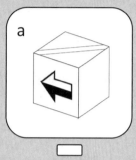

b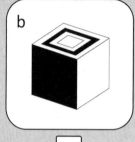

c

d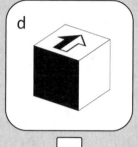

23.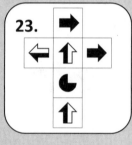

a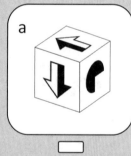

b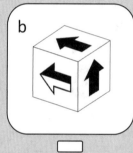

c

d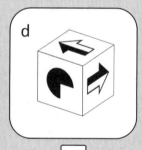

24.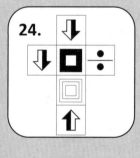

a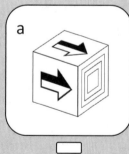

b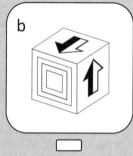

c

d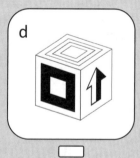

FIRST PAST THE POST® SERIES

3D Non-Verbal Reasoning

Paper 4 - 3D Plan Views

Page	20	21	22	23	24	Total
Mark	/5	/5	/5	/5	/4	/24

Read the following instructions carefully:

1. You have **12 minutes** to complete this test of **24 questions**.

2. Work as quickly and carefully as you can.

3. Once you have finished a page go straight onto the next page until you finish the test.

4. To change an answer, rub out your original answer and mark your new answer clearly.

5. If you are unsure of the answer, choose the one you think is most appropriate or return to it later.

6. Once you have completed the paper go back to any questions you have missed out and check your answers.

Good luck!

After you have finished this paper you can use the 11+ Peer Compare System™ to see how well you performed in comparison to others who have taken this test. You can register by visiting www.ElevenPlusExams.co.uk/FirstPastThePost to post your results anonymously and obtain the feedback.

© 2014 ElevenPlusExams.co.uk   -19-   COPYING STRICTLY PROHIBITED

3D Plan Views

Work out which option is a plan view (bird's-eye view) of the 3D figure on the left.

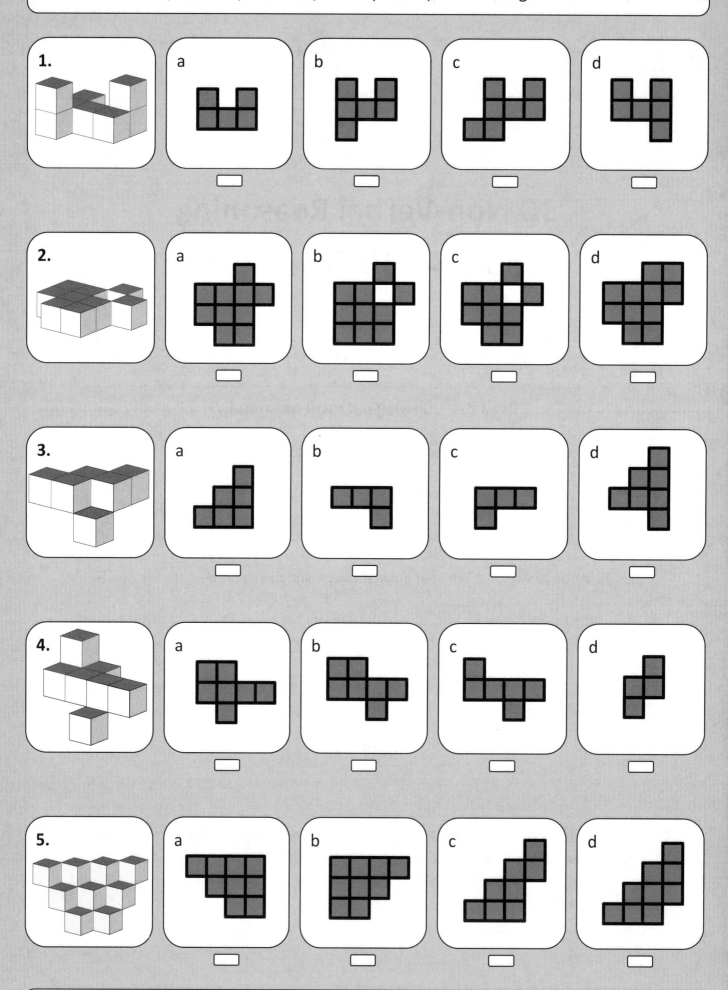

3D Plan Views

Work out which option is a plan view (bird's-eye view) of the 3D figure on the left.

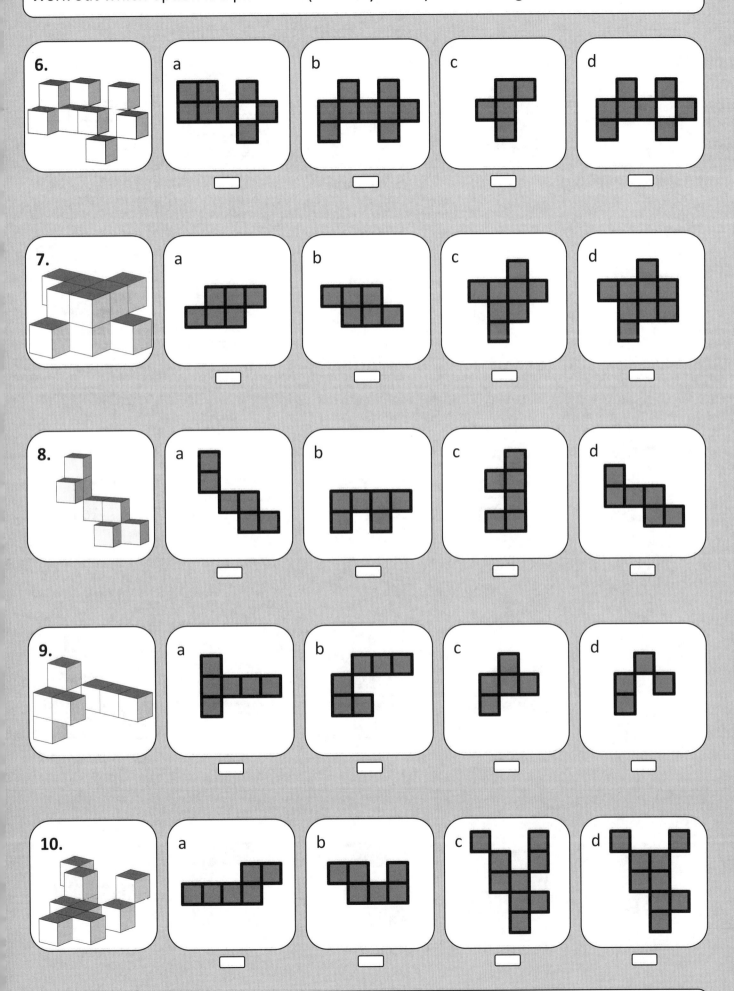

COPYING STRICTLY PROHIBITED

3D Plan Views

Work out which option is a plan view (bird's-eye view) of the 3D figure on the left.

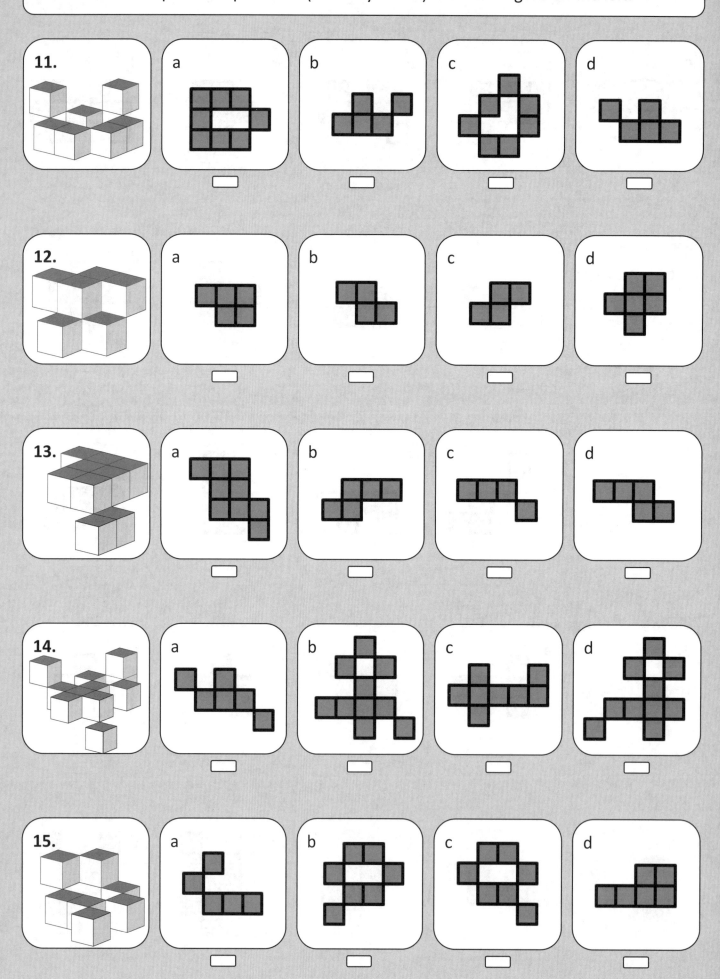

3D Plan Views

Work out which option is a plan view (bird's-eye view) of the 3D figure on the left.

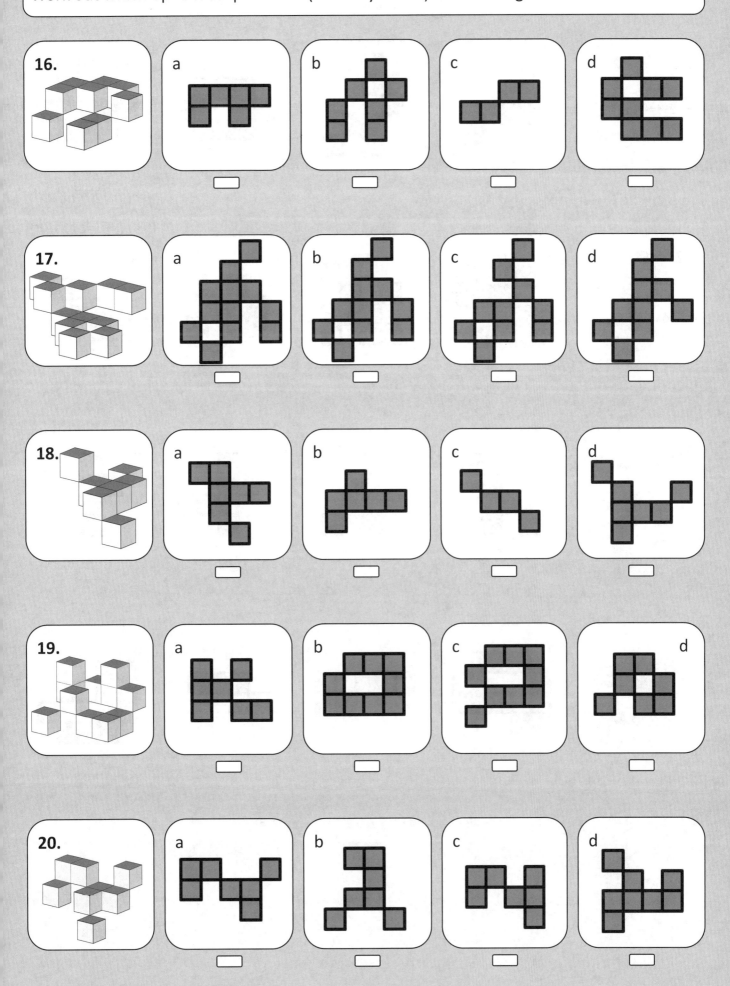

© 2014 ElevenPlusExams.co.uk   COPYING STRICTLY PROHIBITED

3D Plan Views

Work out which option is a plan view (bird's-eye view) of the 3D figure on the left.

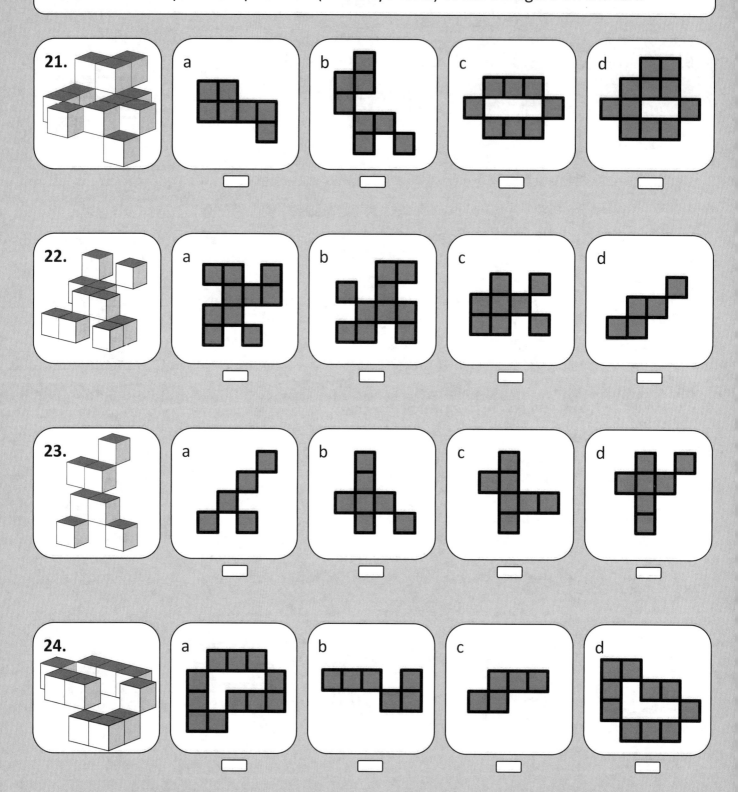

21.   a   b   c   d

22.   a   b   c   d

23.   a   b   c   d

24.   a   b   c   d

FIRST PAST THE POST® SERIES

3D Non-Verbal Reasoning

Mixed Paper 1

Page	26	27	28	29	Total
Mark	/6	/5	/5	/5	/21

Read the following instructions carefully:

1. You have **11 minutes** to complete this test of **21 questions**.

2. Work as quickly and carefully as you can.

3. Once you have finished a page go straight onto the next page until you finish the test.

4. To change an answer, rub out your original answer and mark your new answer clearly.

5. If you are unsure of the answer, choose the one you think is most appropriate or return to it later.

6. Once you have completed the paper go back to any questions you have missed out and check your answers.

Good luck!

After you have finished this paper you can use the 11+ Peer Compare System™ to see how well you performed in comparison to others who have taken this test. You can register by visiting www.ElevenPlusExams.co.uk/FirstPastThePost to post your results anonymously and obtain the feedback.

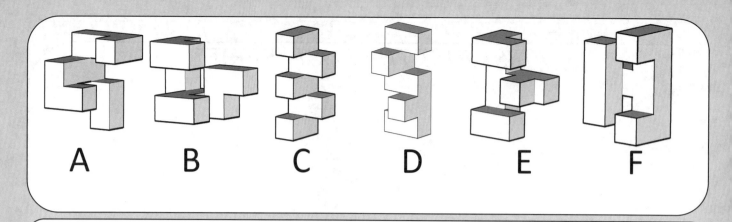

A B C D E F

3D Views

Identify which shape has been rotated by placing a mark in the box next to its corresponding letter, or mark 'None'.

1.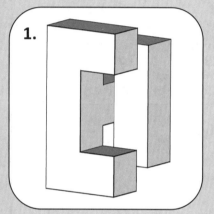

A ☐ D ☐
B ☐ E ☐
C ☐ F ☐
None ☐

2.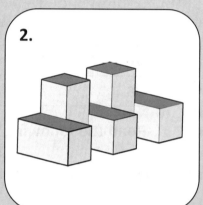

A ☐ D ☐
B ☐ E ☐
C ☐ F ☐
None ☐

3.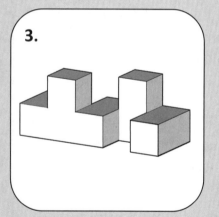

A ☐ D ☐
B ☐ E ☐
C ☐ F ☐
None ☐

4.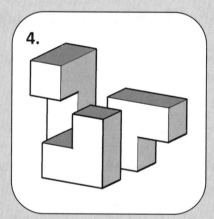

A ☐ D ☐
B ☐ E ☐
C ☐ F ☐
None ☐

5.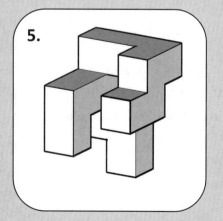

A ☐ D ☐
B ☐ E ☐
C ☐ F ☐
None ☐

6.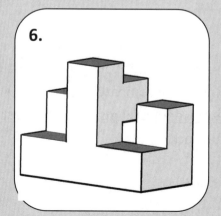

A ☐ D ☐
B ☐ E ☐
C ☐ F ☐
None ☐

3D Composite Shapes

Work out which set of blocks can be put together to make the 3D figure on the left.

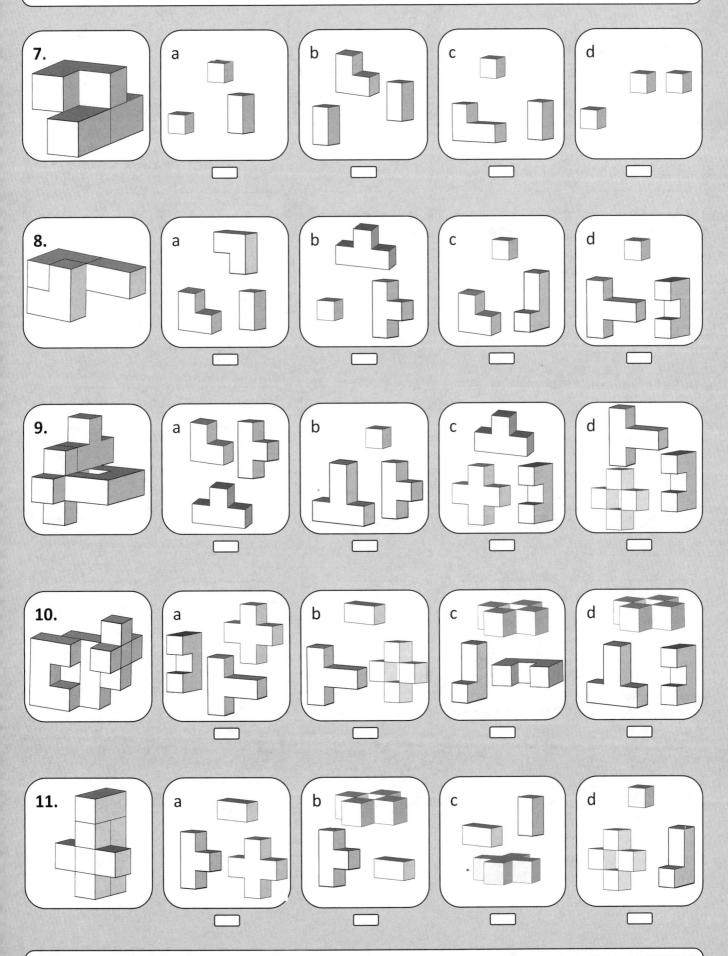

7. a b c d

8. a b c d

9. a b c d

10. a b c d

11. a b c d

3D Cube Nets

Work out which of the four cubes can be made from the net.

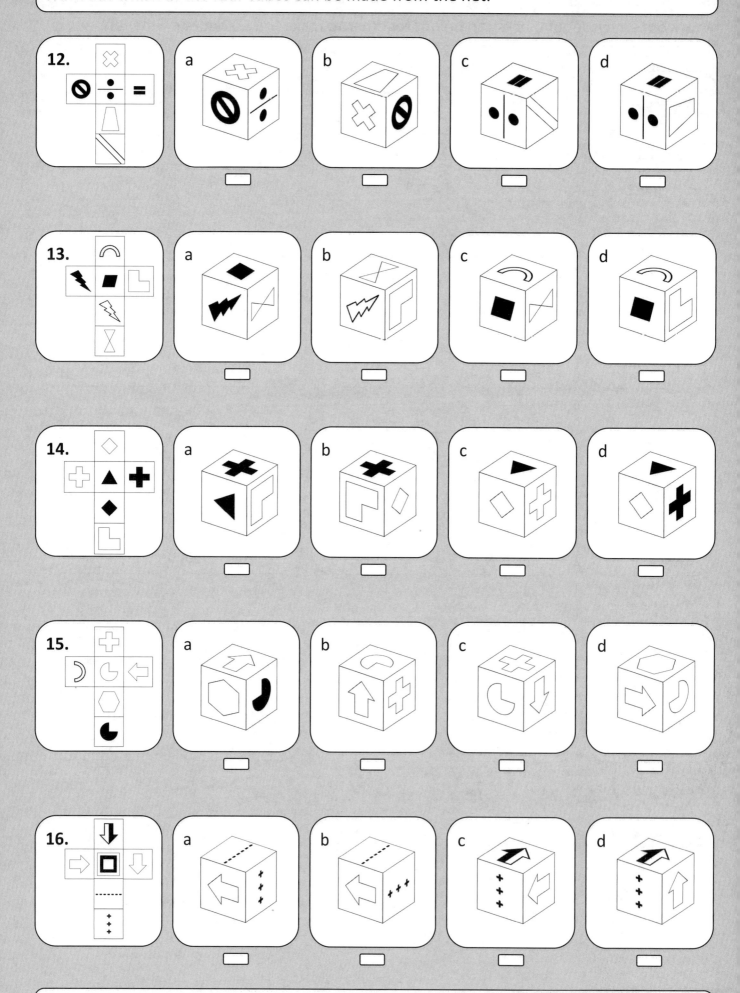

3D Plan Views

Work out which option is a plan view (bird's-eye view) of the 3D figure on the left.

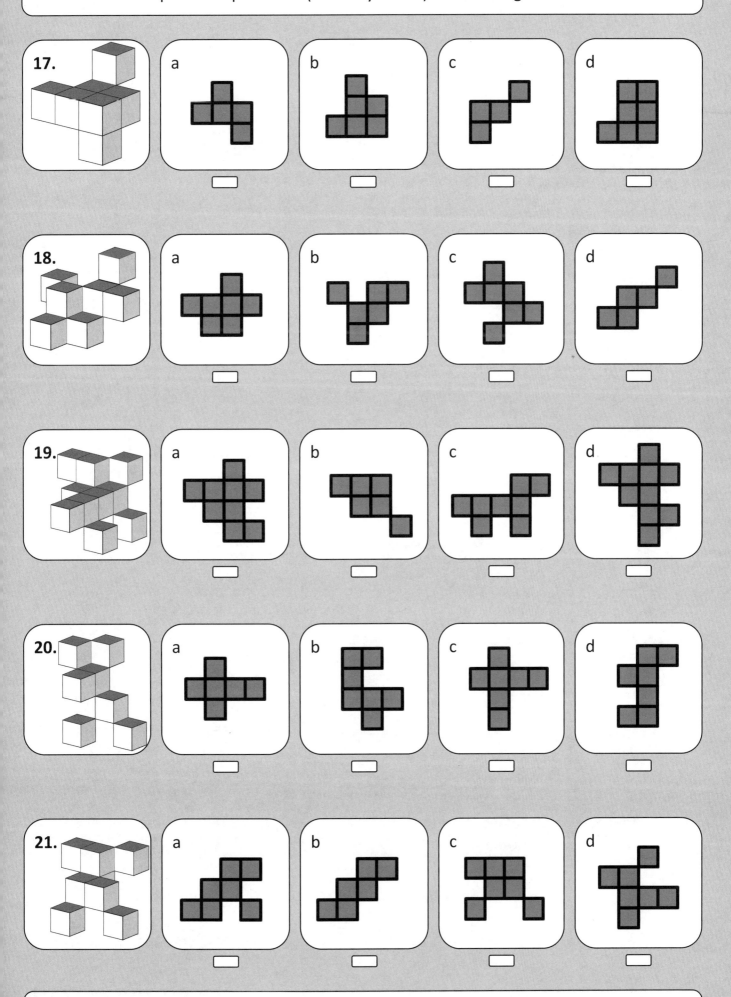

17.   a   b   c   d

18.   a   b   c   d

19.   a   b   c   d

20.   a   b   c   d

21.   a   b   c   d

COPYING STRICTLY PROHIBITED

BLANK PAGE

© 2014 ElevenPlusExams.co.uk

COPYING STRICTLY PROHIBITED

FIRST PAST THE POST® SERIES

3D Non-Verbal Reasoning

Mixed Paper 2

Page	32	33	34	35	Total
Mark	/6	/5	/5	/5	/21

Read the following instructions carefully:

1. You have **11 minutes** to complete this test of **21 questions**.

2. Work as quickly and carefully as you can.

3. Once you have finished a page go straight onto the next page until you finish the test.

4. To change an answer, rub out your original answer and mark your new answer clearly.

5. If you are unsure of the answer, choose the one you think is most appropriate or return to it later.

6. Once you have completed the paper go back to any questions you have missed out and check your answers.

Good luck!

After you have finished this paper you can use the 11+ Peer Compare System™ to see how well you performed in comparison to others who have taken this test. You can register by visiting www.ElevenPlusExams.co.uk/FirstPastThePost to post your results anonymously and obtain the feedback.

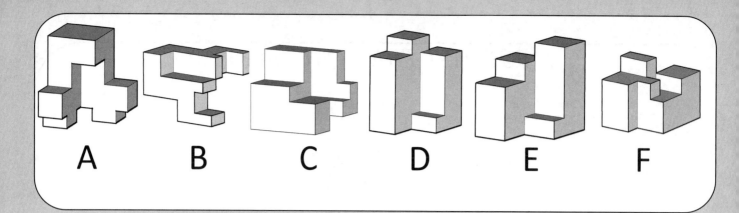

A   B   C   D   E   F

3D Views

Identify which shape has been rotated by placing a mark in the box next to its corresponding letter, or mark 'None'.

1.

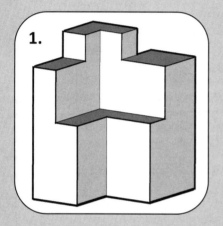

A ☐   D ☐

B ☐   E ☐

C ☐   F ☐

None ☐

2.

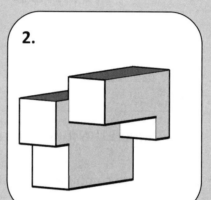

A ☐   D ☐

B ☐   E ☐

C ☐   F ☐

None ☐

3.

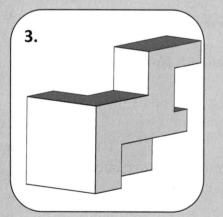

A ☐   D ☐

B ☐   E ☐

C ☐   F ☐

None ☐

4.

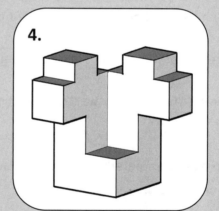

A ☐   D ☐

B ☐   E ☐

C ☐   F ☐

None ☐

5.

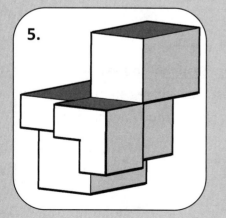

A ☐   D ☐

B ☐   E ☐

C ☐   F ☐

None ☐

6.

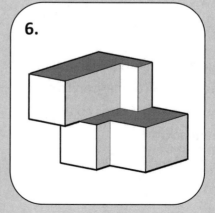

A ☐   D ☐

B ☐   E ☐

C ☐   F ☐

None ☐

3D Composite Shapes

Work out which set of blocks can be put together to make the 3D figure on the left.

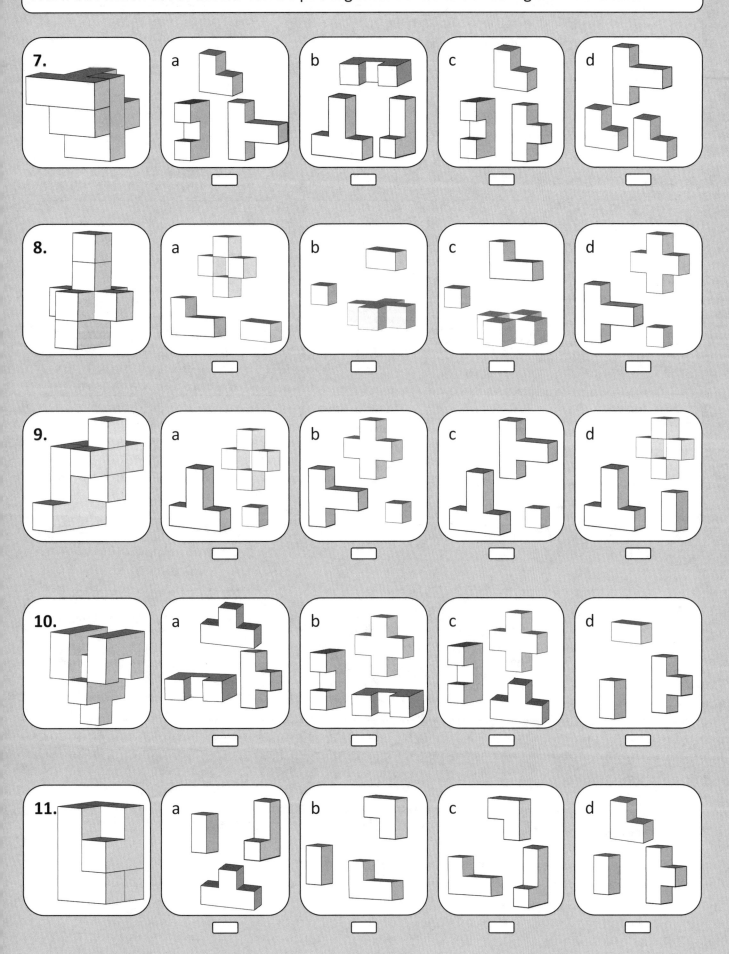

3D Cube Nets

Work out which of the four cubes can be made from the net.

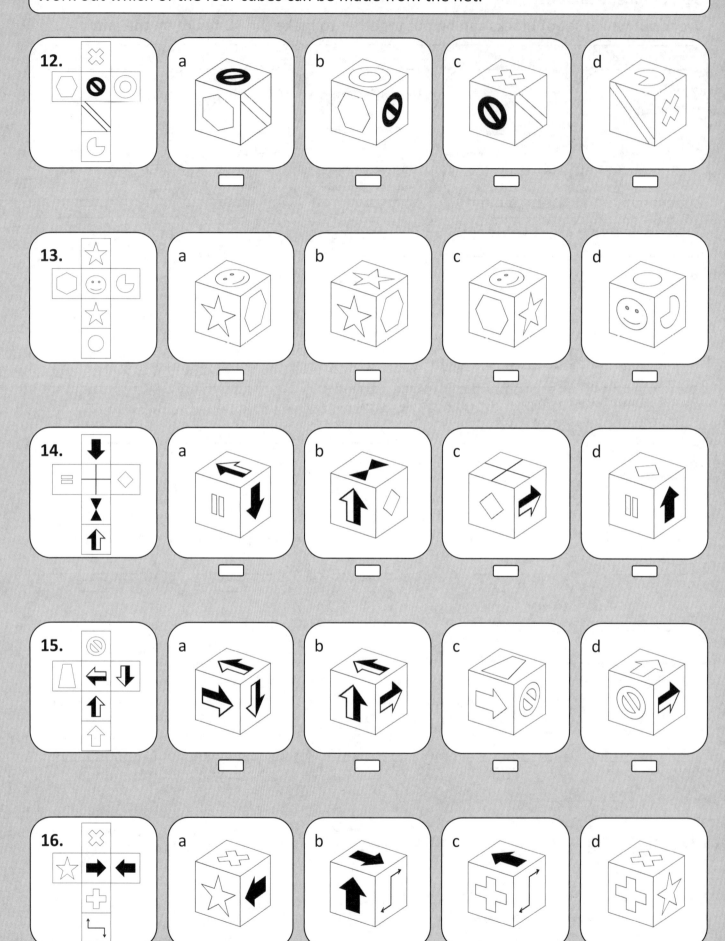

3D Plan Views

Work out which option is a plan view (bird's-eye view) of the 3D figure on the left.

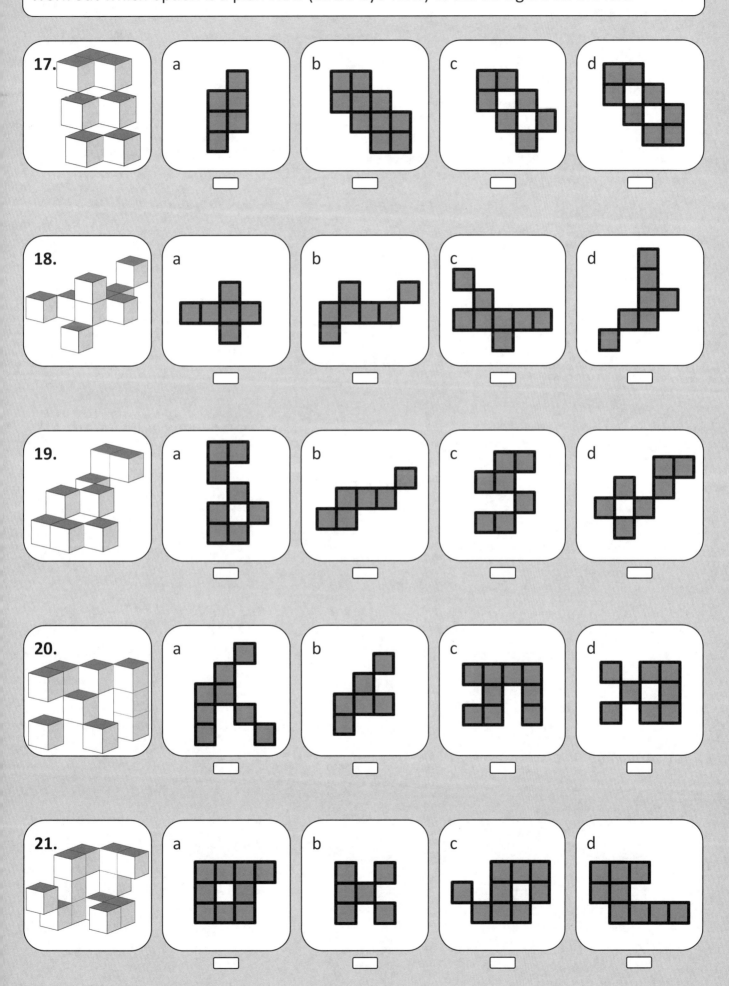

BLANK PAGE

© 2014 ElevenPlusExams.co.uk   COPYING STRICTLY PROHIBITED

FIRST PAST THE POST® SERIES

3D Non-Verbal Reasoning

Mixed Paper 3

Page	38	39	40	41	Total
Mark	/6	/5	/5	/5	/21

Read the following instructions carefully:

1. You have **11 minutes** to complete this test of **21 questions**.

2. Work as quickly and carefully as you can.

3. Once you have finished a page go straight onto the next page until you finish the test.

4. To change an answer, rub out your original answer and mark your new answer clearly.

5. If you are unsure of the answer, choose the one you think is most appropriate or return to it later.

6. Once you have completed the paper go back to any questions you have missed out and check your answers.

Good luck!

After you have finished this paper you can use the 11+ Peer Compare System™ to see how well you performed in comparison to others who have taken this test. You can register by visiting www.ElevenPlusExams.co.uk/FirstPastThePost to post your results anonymously and obtain the feedback.

© 2014 ElevenPlusExams.co.uk

COPYING STRICTLY PROHIBITED

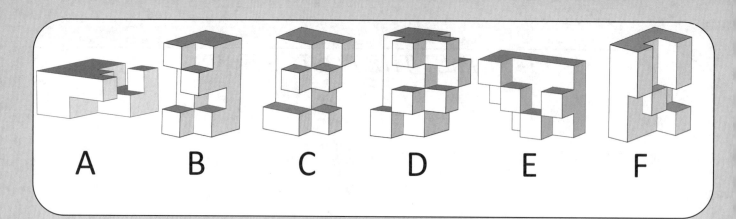

A B C D E F

3D Views

Identify which shape has been rotated by placing a mark in the box next to its corresponding letter, or mark 'None'.

1.

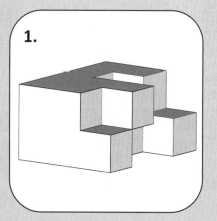

A ☐ D ☐

B ☐ E ☐

C ☐ F ☐

None ☐

2.

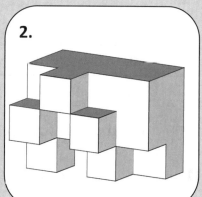

A ☐ D ☐

B ☐ E ☐

C ☐ F ☐

None ☐

3.

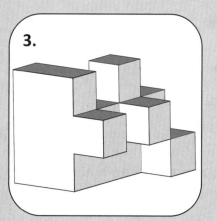

A ☐ D ☐

B ☐ E ☐

C ☐ F ☐

None ☐

4.

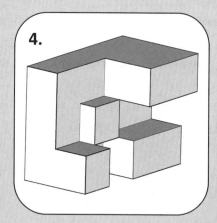

A ☐ D ☐

B ☐ E ☐

C ☐ F ☐

None ☐

5.

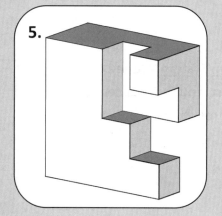

A ☐ D ☐

B ☐ E ☐

C ☐ F ☐

None ☐

6.

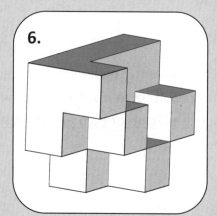

A ☐ D ☐

B ☐ E ☐

C ☐ F ☐

None ☐

3D Composite Shapes

Work out which set of blocks can be put together to make the 3D figure on the left.

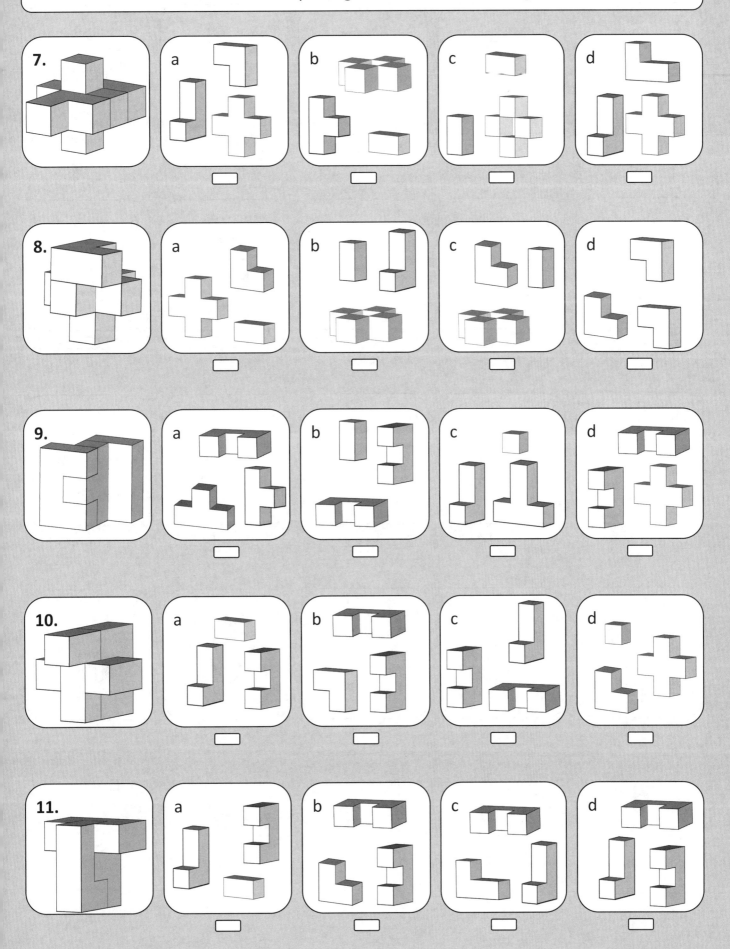

7.   a   b   c   d

8.   a   b   c   d

9.   a   b   c   d

10.   a   b   c   d

11.   a   b   c   d

© 2014 ElevenPlusExams.co.uk   COPYING STRICTLY PROHIBITED

3D Cube Nets

Work out which of the four cubes can be made from the net.

12. 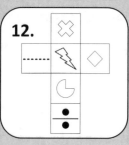 a 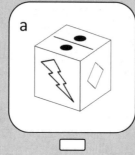 b 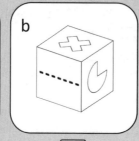 c 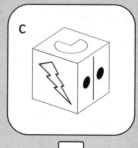 d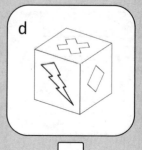

13. 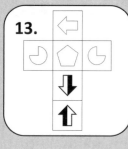 a 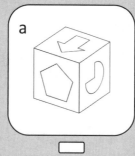 b 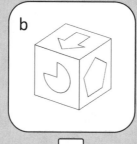 c 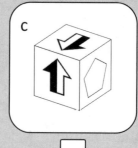 d

14. 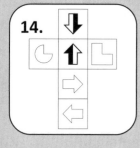 a 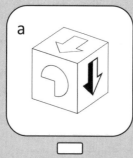 b 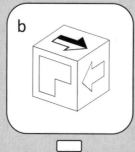 c 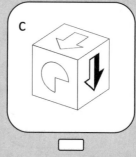 d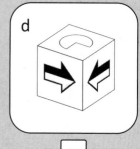

15. 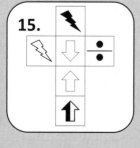 a 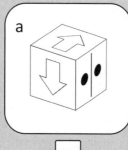 b 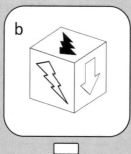 c  d

16.  a 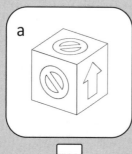 b 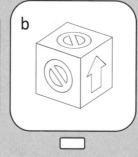 c 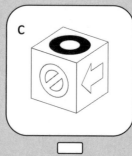 d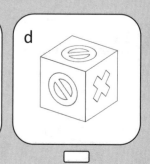

© 2014 ElevenPlusExams.co.uk COPYING STRICTLY PROHIBITED

3D Plan Views

Work out which option is a plan view (bird's-eye view) of the 3D figure on the left.

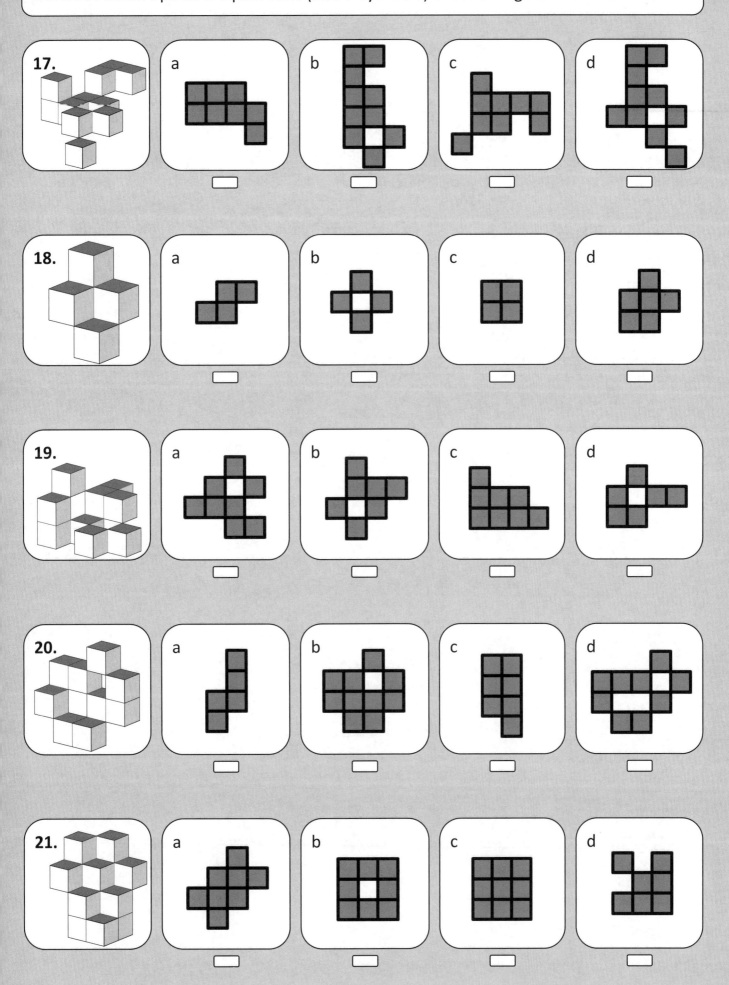

BLANK PAGE

FIRST PAST THE POST® SERIES

3D Non-Verbal Reasoning

Mixed Paper 4

Page	44	45	46	47	Total
Mark	/6	/5	/5	/5	/21

Read the following instructions carefully:

1. You have **11 minutes** to complete this test of **21 questions**.

2. Work as quickly and carefully as you can.

3. Once you have finished a page go straight onto the next page until you finish the test.

4. To change an answer, rub out your original answer and mark your new answer clearly.

5. If you are unsure of the answer, choose the one you think is most appropriate or return to it later.

6. Once you have completed the paper go back to any questions you have missed out and check your answers.

Good luck!

After you have finished this paper you can use the 11+ Peer Compare System™ to see how well you performed in comparison to others who have taken this test. You can register by visiting www.ElevenPlusExams.co.uk/FirstPastThePost to post your results anonymously and obtain the feedback.

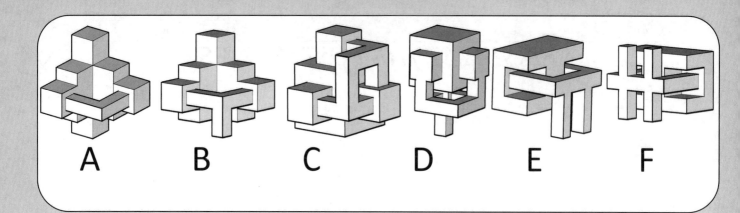

A   B   C   D   E   F

3D Views

Identify which shape has been rotated by placing a mark in the box next to its corresponding letter, or mark 'None'.

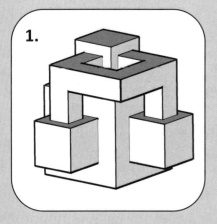

1.

A ☐   D ☐

B ☐   E ☐

C ☐   F ☐

None ☐

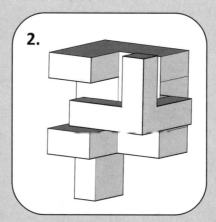

2.

A ☐   D ☐

B ☐   E ☐

C ☐   F ☐

None ☐

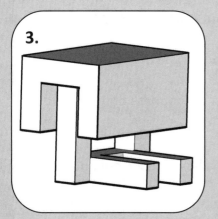

3.

A ☐   D ☐

B ☐   E ☐

C ☐   F ☐

None ☐

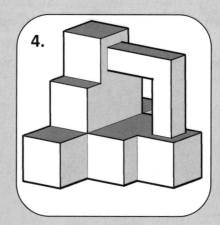

4.

A ☐   D ☐

B ☐   E ☐

C ☐   F ☐

None ☐

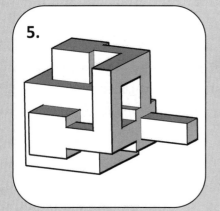

5.

A ☐   D ☐

B ☐   E ☐

C ☐   F ☐

None ☐

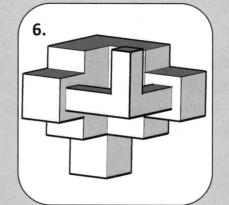

6.

A ☐   D ☐

B ☐   E ☐

C ☐   F ☐

None ☐

© 2014 ElevenPlusExams.co.uk COPYING STRICTLY PROHIBITED

3D Composite Shapes

Work out which set of blocks can be put together to make the 3D figure on the left.

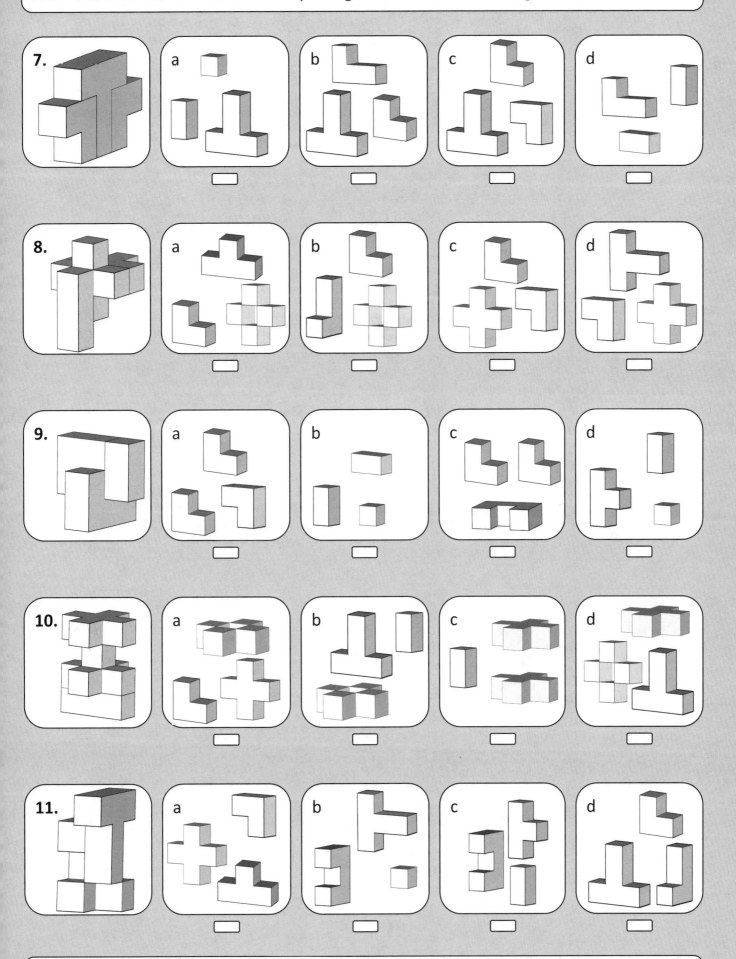

7.   a   b   c   d

8.   a   b   c   d

9.   a   b   c   d

10.   a   b   c   d

11.   a   b   c   d

3D Cube Nets

Work out which of the four cubes can be made from the net.

12. 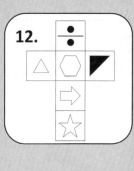 a 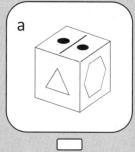 b 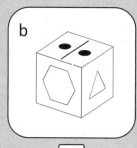 c 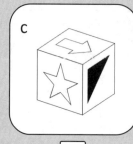 d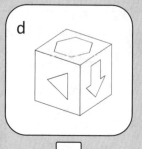

13.  a 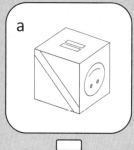 b 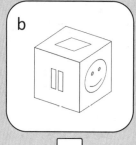 c 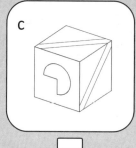 d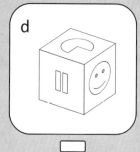

14. 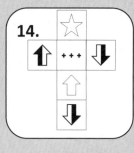 a  b 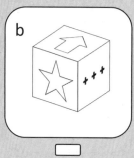 c  d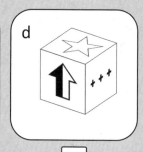

15. 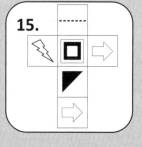 a 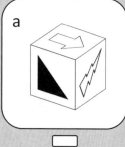 b 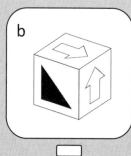 c 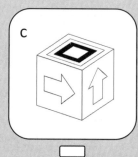 d

16. 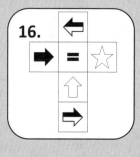 a 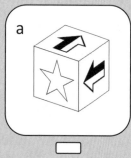 b 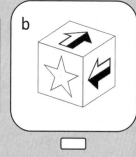 c  d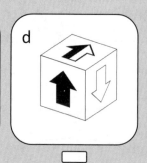

© 2014 ElevenPlusExams.co.uk   COPYING STRICTLY PROHIBITED

3D Plan Views

Work out which option is a plan view (bird's-eye view) of the 3D figure on the left.

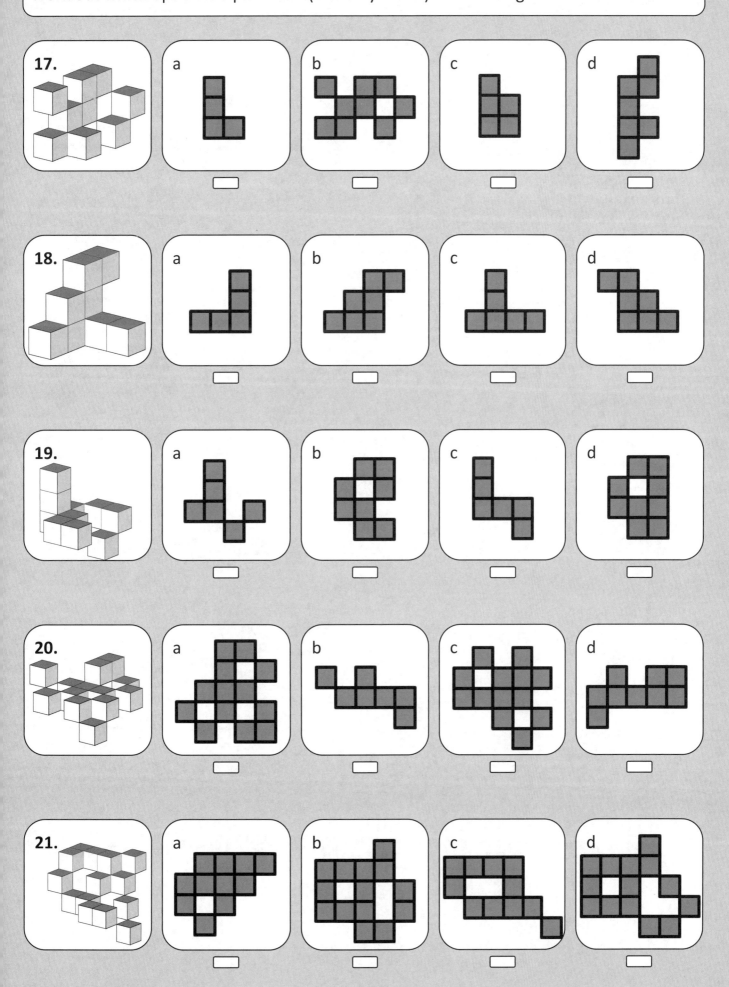

17.　a　b　c　d

18.　a　b　c　d

19.　a　b　c　d

20.　a　b　c　d

21.　a　b　c　d

© 2014 ElevenPlusExams.co.uk　　　COPYING STRICTLY PROHIBITED

BLANK PAGE

FIRST PAST THE POST® SERIES

3D Non-verbal Reasoning

Answers

As you complete each short test, remember that you can use the 11+ Peer Compare System™ to see how well you performed in comparison to others who have taken this test.

You can register by visiting www.ElevenPlusExams.co.uk/FirstPastThePost to post your results anonymously and obtain the feedback.

Your unique 16 digit access code is:

PVF4-3RLG-PI6M-4HHO

Answers and Explanations

Paper 1 - 3D Views

Page 2		Page 3		Page 4		Page 5	
Question	Answer	Question	Answer	Question	Answer	Question	Answer
1	C	7	F	13	None	19	D
2	B	8	D	14	B	20	E
3	F	9	E	15	D	21	B
4	D	10	A	16	C	22	None
5	A	11	None	17	C	23	F
6	B	12	A	18	None	24	E

Paper 2 - 3D Composite Shapes

Page 8		Page 9		Page 10		Page 11		Page 12	
Question	Answer	Question	Answer	Question	Answer	Question	Answer	Question	Answer
1	b	6	b	11	b	16	c	21	b
2	c	7	b	12	c	17	a	22	c
3	d	8	a	13	d	18	b	23	a
4	a	9	c	14	a	19	c	24	c
5	b	10	d	15	b	20	b		

Paper 3 - 3D Cube Nets

Page 14		Page 15		Page 16		Page 17		Page 18	
Question	Answer	Question	Answer	Question	Answer	Question	Answer	Question	Answer
1	c	6	c	11	c	16	c	21	c
2	b	7	d	12	a	17	b	22	b
3	d	8	b	13	a	18	c	23	d
4	c	9	a	14	d	19	d	24	a
5	a	10	d	15	d	20	a		

© 2014 ElevenPlusExams.co.uk   COPYING STRICTLY PROHIBITED

Paper 4 - 3D Plan Views

Page 20		Page 21		Page 22		Page 23		Page 24	
Question	Answer	Question	Answer	Question	Answer	Question	Answer	Question	Answer
1	b	6	d	11	c	16	d	21	d
2	c	7	c	12	d	17	b	22	b
3	a	8	b	13	a	18	a	23	c
4	b	9	b	14	b	19	c	24	d
5	d	10	c	15	c	20	d		

Mixed Paper 1

Page 26		Page 27		Page 28		Page 29	
Question	Answer	Question	Answer	Question	Answer	Question	Answer
1	F	7	b	12	a	17	b
2	C	8	a	13	d	18	c
3	D	9	c	14	c	19	d
4	A	10	d	15	b	20	a
5	None	11	b	16	a	21	d
6	E						

Mixed Paper 2

Page 32		Page 33		Page 34		Page 35	
Question	Answer	Question	Answer	Question	Answer	Question	Answer
1	C	7	b	12	a	17	c
2	D	8	c	13	c	18	c
3	B	9	d	14	a	19	a
4	A	10	b	15	d	20	b
5	None	11	c	16	c	21	d
6	E						

Mixed Paper 3

Page 38		Page 39		Page 40		Page 41	
Question	Answer	Question	Answer	Question	Answer	Question	Answer
1	B	7	b	12	d	17	d
2	D	8	c	13	b	18	c
3	C	9	d	14	c	19	a
4	None	10	c	15	c	20	c
5	A	11	b	16	d	21	c
6	E						

Mixed Paper 4

Page 44		Page 45		Page 46		Page 47	
Question	Answer	Question	Answer	Question	Answer	Question	Answer
1	C	7	c	12	a	17	d
2	None	8	b	13	c	18	c
3	E	9	c	14	d	19	b
4	A	10	d	15	b	20	a
5	D	11	b	16	b	21	d
6	B						

© 2014 ElevenPlusExams.co.uk   COPYING STRICTLY PROHIBITED